£4.25

ISBN 0-85116-584-2

THE JOYS of NOISE!

YOU'VE HEARD OF "THE BODY SHOP" WELL, DENNIS PLANS TO OPEN . . .

. . . THE BEASTIE SHOP

DAD

MENACE STYLE HEDGEHOG WIG

OCTOPUS DREADLOCK WIG

BERTIE BLENKINSOP

MOTH DUST EYE SHADOW

NERVOUS REX

SOFTY WALTER

SPOTTY PERKINS

SPIDER LEG EYELASHES

SNAIL SLIME EYELID SOOTHERS

WORKER ANT SPOTS

CATERPILLAR EYEBROWS — AVAILABLE IN A VARIETY OF EXPRESSIONS

CURLY

PIE-FACE

MUM

THE "I'VE JUST BOUGHT A COPY OF THE BEANO" LOOK

THE "NO PIES LEFT" LOOK

THE "WHERE HAVE MY EYEBROWS GONE?" LOOK

SUMMING UP

BOO-HOO-HOO!

WHAT'S WRONG WITH THAT SOFTY?

THERE, THERE, WALTER!

I GOT A SUM WRONG! SOB! SOB!

HUH! DON'T WORRY— I GOT THAT ONE WRONG, TOO.

YES, BUT YOU GOT THE OTHER 999 WRONG AS WELL!

BAH!

I'LL HAVE TO DO TEN HOURS' EXTRA STUDYING TONIGHT!

Later—

HUH! HOW BORING! NO-ONE TO MENACE WHILE WALTER'S INSIDE STUDYING.

FED UP

ALL CHANGE

WHAT A MESS YOU'RE IN! WHY NOT TRY SOMETHING NICE AND SAFE—LIKE BIRDWATCHING?

WALTER, PRINCE OF SOFTIES

SKIP

AND YOU, M'LAD—YOU'RE TOO SOFT!

FEATHER

OUCH!

STAGGER

I WANT YOU TO DO A LITTLE MENACING. HERE—A WATER PISTOL, A CATAPULT, A PEASHOOTER—AND DON'T FORGET TO THROW A CUSTARD PIE OR TWO!

HAW-HAW-HAW!

I DON'T KNOW WHY YOU'RE LAUGHING—GET BIRDWATCHING!

OH, DEARIE, DEARIE ME!

HAW-HAW!

HERE COMES PIE-FACE. I SUPPOSE I COULD TRY HITTING HIM WITH A CUSTARD PIE!

MENACE

OH, IT'S HEAVY—BUT I'VE MANAGED TO THROW A SLICE!

SOFT THROW

EH?

CHOMP! SLURP! THANKS VERY MUCH, WALTER!

NEXT DOOR—

I'LL JUST HAVE A CHOC OR TWO BEFORE I GO TO MY SLIMMERS' CLASS.

SHRIEK! A HUGE, HORRIBLE SPIDER! HERE—T-TAKE THIS!

WELL DONE, GNASHER! THIS LOT WILL GET RASHER NICE AND FAT!

ON THE OTHER HAND, HE DOESN'T NEED ALL THESE CHOCS, DOES HE?

CHOMP! CHOMP!

CHOCS

SORRY, RASHER!

EMPTY

RAGE

Soon—

NOW REMEMBER, SLIMMERS—NO CHEATING ON YOUR DIET.

SLIMMERS' CLUB

N-O-O-O!

CAKE SHOP

SLIMMERS' CLUB

TO THE CAKE SHOP GIRLS!

HMMM!

Presently—

SLIMMERS CLUB

EEK!

SOLD OUT

EEK!

YIKES!

CLANG!

CLANG!

WHAT'S THAT NOISE? AHA—CAUGHT MY CLASS CHEATING!

CHOMP! OINK! CHOMP!

The day of the show—

CRASH!

MENACES' HUT

WOW! DON'T SAY THE MENACES HAVE WON A HEAVY TROPHY THAT'S CRASHED THROUGH THE SHELVES LIKE MINE DID!

TEE-HEE! RASHER'S SO FAT, HE'S GONE STRAIGHT THROUGH THE FLOOR!

WE'LL NEVER GET HIM OUT IN TIME FOR THE SHOW!

STUCK FAST

HUP-TWO-THREE-FOUR! HUP-TWO-THREE-FOUR!

WHO CAN THAT BE?

NACES' HUT

HERE'S A REWARD FOR YOU AND YOUR PIG, FOR KEEPING MY CLUB MEMBERS SLIM!

PUFF!

PANT!

THAT MONEY WILL HELP US GET MUCH FATTER!

BAH!

Then—

BUBBLE GUM

POP!

WHERE'S REX GONE NOW?

IT WAS THE BUBBLE BURSTING—HE'S TERRIFIED BY LOUD NOISES!

HOWL!

WHAT'S WRONG NOW?

I'M SCARED OF H-HEIGHTS, T-TOO!

THANKS, DENNIS!

I CAN'T PLAY "STATUES" AT PARTIES—I SHAKE SO MUCH!

AND I ALWAYS SPILL MY LUNCH!

TEACHER CAN'T READ MY WRITING EITHER!

NEVER MIND—THERE IS ONE ADVANTAGE—TAKE THIS!

GNASH!

SLURP! SLURP!

YOU MAKE GREAT MILK SHAKES!

GLAD I WAS OF SOME USE, DENNIS!

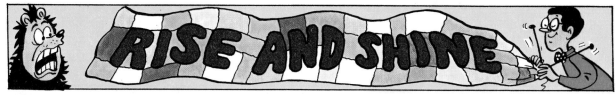

GET YOUR SKATES ON

One chilly day—

NOW TO SHOOT!

OOPS!

RUMBLE!

ERK!

SQUASH!

THE BALL'S MORE LIKE A PUCK NOW! LET'S PLAY ICE HOCKEY.

BUT WE DON'T HAVE SKATES!

OR STICKS!

Soon—

SUCH FUN!

WALTER, THE SOPPY SOFT BOY

WE'LL BORROW THESE!

YIKES! MY BOATS!

At the pond—

THESE WORK PERFECTLY!

NOW FOR THE STICKS!

SNOW JOKE

THAT DOG, GNASHER...

...RACED THROUGH A PUDDLE AND SPLASHED ME!

...TRIPPED ME UP...

OH, DEAR!

YOU'LL HAVE TO PUT THAT PEST ON A LEAD. I'VE HAD TOO MANY COMPLAINTS.

AW, DAD — GNASHER DOESN'T LIKE BEING ON A LEAD!

Soon—

GNASHER'S ON A LEAD, DAD — CAN WE GO OUT TO PLAY?

AH, THAT'S BETTER — NO MORE COMPLAINTS. OFF YOU GO, MY BOY.

SNIGGER! DAD DIDN'T SAY HOW LONG THE LEAD HAD TO BE! NOW FOR SOME FUN!

GNEE-HEE!

Shortly—

OH, BOY! THE SOFTIES ARE GOING TO BUY SWEETS!

SWEET SHOP

THESE ARE GOING TO BE SPIFFING, CHUMMIES.

OPEN

HOP

SWEETS

HOW NICE OF YOU TO SHARE YOUR SWEETS WITH US, WALTER!

HOP

SWEETS

GRAB

CLUNK!

ZONK!

SPLAT!

So—

PLOP! PLOP!

SWEETS SWEETS

Meanwhile—

DENNIS TRIPPED US UP WITH A LONG LEAD!

HE DID, DID HE?

FROM NOW ON, GNASHER'S TO BE ON A SHORT LEAD, MY LAD — OR ELSE!

Shortly—

WE SPOILED YOUR FUN! NYA-NAH-NAH-NAH-NAH!

DON'T YOU BELIEVE IT!

PYOING! ZIP!

EH?

HOWL!

SPLOT!

ELDERLY TOMATO

WHIMPER! YOUR NAUGHTY SON FIRED A CATAPULT AT ME AND HIT ME!

GRRR! THIS HAS GONE TOO FAR!

ALL RIGHT — WHERE'S THE CATAPULT?

CATAPULT? I DON'T HAVE A CATAPULT — YOU CAN SEARCH ME.

BOO-HOO! BUT HE *DID* HAVE ONE — I HEARD IT!

I HAVE MY SUSPICIONS — HAVE A NICE BICCY, GNASHER!

ERK! NO!

SO! AN ELASTIC LEAD!

ERK! NO!

PYOING

THAT'S WHAT HE USED TO FIRE AT ME, THE ROTTER!

I SEE WHERE I WENT WRONG — WE SHOULDN'T HAVE PUT GNASHER ON A LEAD.

QUITE RIGHT, DAD — I TOLD YOU HE DOESN'T LIKE LEADS.

Soon— YES — WE PUT THE WRONG PEST ON A LEAD!

WALKIES, DENNIS? TEE-HEE! TITTER!

BABY REINS

HMPH! I DON'T LIKE LEADS EITHER! THE SHAME OF IT — I'LL NEVER LIVE THIS DOWN!

WHAT I DID ON MY

Dad was acting very strange. He put on his Hawaiian shirt that looks as if Rasher has had his dinner off it. It looks like this because I tried to get Rasher to have his dinner off it once but the pattern was so bad that it made even Rasher lose his appetite. I was going to put on some summery clothes too but Dad would not let me.

"You've got to go in fancy dress – it's a rule they have for children at the place we're going." I didn't have any fancy dress clothes but luckily my Dad just happened to have a dog suit that fitted me and was very realistic.

Eventually I managed to make myself heard. She didn't believe what I told her though. She thought I was far too badly behaved to be a human but she was very surprised to have a dog that talked in her kennels. She got on to a television company straight away.

Soon I was famous. I appeared on game shows. I bit Esther Ranzen on "Bark of Gold" and I chased Noel Edmonds up a tree (just for fun – this wasn't on TV) Postmen everywhere hated me. Not only could I bite their trousers like a normal dog – I could make hurtful remarks about the colour of their socks too.

HOLIDAYS

First we had to drop Gnasher and Gnipper off at the kennels. I was puzzled when the woman in charge talked about the three kennels that had been reserved because I know that Gnasher and Gnipper only come to two. Dad said there were three dogs - Gnasher, Gnipper and me! She believed him, grabbed my leash, and led me to the kennels.

I tried to tell her that I wasn't a dog but she couldn't hear me for the whoops of joy that came from Mum and Dad as they ran away. When they were gone I tried to tell the woman again but this time I was drowned out by Gnasher and Gnipper, laughing at me.

Eventually Mum and Dad came back from holiday and told everyone the truth, the spoilsports. They took my dog suit and sent me back to school. I might not like school, but it was even worse in a dog obedience school - especially when it came to eating my playtime snack.

School

DOG

DOG

At school—

DISCO DANCE COMPETITION

OH! GOODY— I'M SURE TO WIN!

WALTER— VERY SOFT

SEE HOW GOOD I AM!

HMPH! HAVE TO BEAT THAT SHOW-OFF.

LIKE TO BE ABLE TO LEAP TEN FEET IN THE AIR AND DO THE SPLITS?

RATHER!

10 FOOT JUMP

SQUEAL! A MOUSE!

HAR-HAR! NOW YOU CAN DO IT!

STOP THIS! YOU HAVE TO HAVE A PARTNER ANYWAY.

So—

WOULD YOU DO ME THE GREAT HONOUR, MADAM?

HOW PERFECTLY CHARMING!

HOW PERFECTLY REVOLTING!

HUH! I'LL GET A MUCH BETTER PARTNER!

HOW'S THAT?

GNESH! GNESH!

BING BONG'S SING SONG

WHAT A FIND

Dennis' Mum and Dad were feeling nervous. No, they weren't waiting on the latest bill from Mr Putty the Beanotown glazier or expecting the local wrestling club at the door demanding that Dennis unties them.

No!

They were nervous because it was quiet. Now, normally, this would have been a cause for rejoicing — but Dennis was in his room with Gnasher. What was he up to? A sponsored silence? Writing an apology to Walter's mum for frightening her budgie by making it sleep in her cat tray?

No!

Dennis was making a model. He was great at it. Gnasher was getting involved too. He wasn't helping Dennis — just trying to get the glue off his paws.

Mum was glad to see Dennis' creation. It was a magnificent, shiny, futuristic example of fantasy space flight. "It's a magnificent, shiny, futuristic example of fantasy flight," Mum said not surprisingly.

"Thanks, Mum, but I'm even better at firing catapults!" said Dennis, producing a multiple catapult loaded with corks. "S-C-R-E-A-M-!" screamed Mum as Dennis ran to the window, armed with his awesome fighting weapon.

Just then, the Beanotown brass band were booming and banging, bassooning and bugling, blowing and brum-brumming along the street.

"A perfect chance to try out my creation," said Dennis, aiming his multiple catapult out of the window.

SHOOOOOM! The corks flew through the air at the speed of sound, drowning out the band until — THWACK! BUNG! KI-CHING! BLURP! Five of the corks flew down the funnel of the bassoon poor Bertie Leatherlungs was about to blow with all his might. Bertie, who had always enjoyed Heavy Metal, turned Deep Purple. (Ask your parents to explain this joke.)

"OO-ER!" Dennis exclaimed. "We'd better get out of here fast, Gnasher!"

"GNESH! GNISHED GNUTTER GNAP!" agreed Gnasher (I think).

So, off they sped as fast as Linford Christie with his shorts aflame.

Soon they came across people digging in a field.

"Who are you and can we help?" Dennis asked one of the men. "We're archaeologists and we're looking for an ancient Roman fort. No." "No?" asked Dennis, "No what?" "No, you can't help us — we've heard all about you." And with that, the archaeologist scooped Dennis and Gnasher up with his spade and tossed them into the air.

Gnasher quickly dug the hole bigger for his master to enter. "Coo! Look! This must be what the archaeologists are looking for!" said Dennis as he emerged into an underground chamber.

They looked down at the mosaic floor. It showed a picture of a familiar-looking character in red and black with spikey hair being chased by angry people wearing togas. Dennis pointed and laughed, "There were menaces around in bygone days too! Chortle!"

Dennis' eyes lit up like Blackpool illuminations on a cold, dark, autumn night. "A SIEGE CATAPULT! THE ULTIMATE MENACE MACHINE!" he beamed.

Dennis crashed into a bush but then made a discovery. No, it wasn't some priceless artefact — he discovered that nettles can be very painful when landed on. A valuable discovery indeed.

"Gnasher! Gnasher! Where are you?" yelled Dennis to his faithful hound. The obedient dog emerged from a hole beside the bush. "Gnasher, you look different somehow," remarked Dennis. Gnasher pointed to the Roman helmet which now adorned his head. "Wow! Where did you get that hat? Where did you get that hat?" sang the Menace.

So Dennis and Gnasher began to load the catapult with the many ancient artefacts that were lying around. They loaded it with shields, coins, sandals and robes. "Be careful not to damage any of that broken pottery, Gnasher!" Dennis joked. When the catapult was full, Dennis released the trigger, firing the findings out of the mouth of the enlarged entrance hole.

Dennis and Gnasher emerged to great applause from the archaeologists. "You're a wonder with a catapult, Dennis!" remarked the chief digger. "The only thing is — we are puzzled by these mud-covered items, Dennis. We don't know what they are," he said. Gnasher whispered into Dennis' ear, "GNISHY WHISPY GNOSHY GNIP!" There was no need to whisper because nobody could tell what he was saying anyway. "Ah! I see!" said Dennis. "Leave it to us, Mr Digger," said Dennis carrying the mud-covered items into the cave.

RUMBLE

PONK

BANG! HAMMER! SCREW! DRILL! DRILL! SCREW! HAMMER! BANG!

"What on earth were Dennis and Gnasher up to?" thought the team, until they charged out of the cave in a Roman chariot with Gnasher pulling it along.

Dennis pelted the archaeologists with mud bombs shouting. "LOOK WHAT I'VE MADE — A ROMAN CHARIOT! I TOLD YOU I WAS GOOD AT MODEL MAKING!"

Back home, Dennis' Dad had calmed down after the cork incident and was feeling peckish.

"I fancy an Italian carry out," he said to Mum.

Just then there was a loud splintering of wood as the front door got rather in the way of the charging charioteers returning home.

"Well," said Mum searching for a witty punchline. "I don't know about an Italian CARRYOUT — but would an Italian CHARIOT do instead?!!"

RUMBLE

WISH I COULD GET RID OF THESE MICE.

SQUEAK!

SQUEAK!

SQUEAK!

GNASHER WILL CLEAR THEM FOR YOU!

GNESH!

GNASH! GNASH!

SQUEAK!

GNASH! GNASH!

WE'RE OFF!

WE GOT RID OF THE MICE FOR YOU.

BAH! YOU ALSO GOT RID OF MY HAYSTACK!

FLATTENED

OO-ER!

Later—

WISH I COULD GET RID OF...

WE'LL DO IT FOR YOU!

...THESE LEAVES IN THE GARDEN!

Later—

OOH! MY BACK! THIS ISN'T WHAT "RENTACLEAR" WAS MEANT FOR!

ACHE

RIGHT, NOW YOU CAN CLEAR...

GROAN!

ACHE

ACHE!

...THESE PLATES!

CHOMP! CLEARLY A GOOD IDEA!

CHOMP! GNESH!

WHAT A STINKER

SOFTY WALTER →

WALTER'S ALWAYS SWOTTING!

GASP! SWOTTING, DENNIS?

ADVANCED PHYSICS

SWATTING, DAD!

SPLAT!

YOU SHOULD ALWAYS BE TRYING TO LEARN. WALTER EVEN DOES SO WHEN HE'S ASLEEP!

WHIRR!

2 x 12 = 24
3 x 12 = 36

I'M OFF TO LEARN THINGS!

"BULLSEYE" BLOGGS

CLUNK!
CLUNK!
CLUNK!

TEACH ME TO THROW LIKE YOU, "BULLSEYE"!

So— HEAD STILL, EYE ON THE TARGET, SLOWLY BACK AND...

...RIGHT ON TARGET! JUST AS "BULLSEYE" TAUGHT ME!

SQUEAL!

ANTIQUE TOMATO

LOOKS like TROUBLE

LOTS OF PEOPLE LOOK LIKE THEIR PETS.

SCREECH!
YAP! YAP!
YAP! YAP!
AND ACT LIKE THEM.

DENNIS DOESN'T LOOK MUCH LIKE ME, THOUGH.
...ZZZZ...

EEK!
I'LL SOON SORT THAT.

...ZZZZ...
PUSH

OINKHA! IDEAL!
FAKE DRACULA FANGS
COOOEE, MUM!
SQUEAL! YOU AND YOUR SILLY TRICKS!

GLOOP!
SNATCH!

PLOP

HMM! NOT QUITE THERE.

THUMP

PERFECT! EXACTLY LIKE ME!
GROO!

MUM THINKS SO TOO!

HAIR AFFAIR

AMN'T I LOOKING IN THE PINK?

SUPER! HOW DID YOU GET YOUR HAIR LIKE THAT, WALTER?

SOFT LITTLE FELLOWS

I GOT THESE LOVELY WASH-OUT HAIR COLOURANTS TO TRY.

WASH-OUT, EH?

I'LL SEE IF THEY WORK!

ULP!

SWOOSH!

THEY DO!

HELP! MUMSIE!

HAIR COLOURANTS

I'LL BORROW THESE.

HAIR COLOURANTS

Later—

GOOD! NO SIGN OF GNASHER.

HEH-HEH! I USED THAT HAIR COLOURANT TO CAMOUFLAGE GNASHER!

GNASH! GNASH!

SCREECH!

WHITE FRIGHT

MY SHEEPDOG'S NOT WELL. COULD YOU GET GNASHER TO ROUND UP MY FLOCK?

EH? ALL RIGHT, FARMER PIGG.

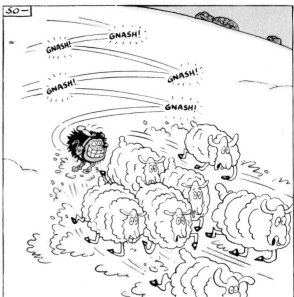

SO—

GNASH! GNASH! GNASH! GNASH! GNASH! GNASH!

WELL DONE, GNASHER!

MEH! MEH! MEH! MEH! MEH!

OOPS—I'VE MISSED ONE!

GNASH! GNASH! GNASH! GNASH! GNASH! GNASH! GNASH!

WOOF! WOOF!

GNEH?

HEH! HEH! THAT'S NOT A SHEEP—IT'S A PYRENEAN MOUNTAIN DOG!

I'M OVER HERE ON HOLIDAY.

MUM'S the WORD

7 a.m.—

OH, NO! ANOTHER DAY WITH MY AWFUL FAMILY!

DENNIS'S MUM

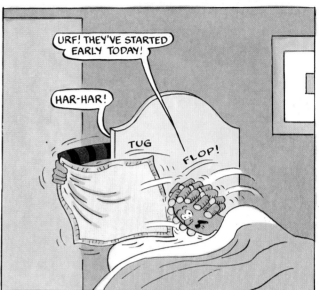

URF! THEY'VE STARTED EARLY TODAY!

HAR-HAR!

TUG

FLOP!

GREAT PILLOW FIGHT!

I'M FOREVER CLEARING UP BEHIND THEM.

AND MY VACUUM CLEANER SUCKS UP SO MUCH RUBBISH...

...IT'S GOT A WEIGHT PROBLEM!

STRAIN

BULGE

SUCK

NICE 'N' KNEESY

SNORES GALORE

RASHER'S PIG OF A CROSSWORD!

The crossword grid (completed):

- 1 Down: MUD
- 2 Across: TURNNIPS
- 3 Down: SNORT
- 4 Down: HAMLET
- 5 Across: BACON
- 6 Down: BURP
- 7 Across: PIGTAILS
- 7 Down: PIGLET
- 8 Across: PIGGLES
- 9 Down: STY
- 10 Across: TROTTER

ACROSS

2. When do I know it's tea-time? Dad's got ------- in his trousers (7)
5. Did you hear about the pig chef? He was always ----- (5)
7. Some girls wear them on their heads and I've got one on my bottom (8)
8. What does a pig do when it hears a joke? It gets a fit of the ------- (7)
10. If a human has a foot, what do I have? (7)

DOWN

1. Great for rolling in (3)
3. The noise I make with my snout (4)
4. My favourite Shakespeare play (6)
6. The noise I make after meal times (4)
7. The name for a baby pig (6)
9. My home and what Dennis's bedroom looks like (3)

ANSWERS

ACROSS—2. TURNIPS, 5. BACON, 7. PIGTAILS, 8. PIGGLES, 10. TROTTER.

DOWN: 1. MUD, 3. SNORT, 4. HAMLET, 6. BURP, 7. PIGLET, 9. STY.

 # THAT'S the STYLE

ONE OF DAD'S COLLARS WILL DO INSTEAD.

SNIP!

OO! I'VE GOT JUST THE THING TO GO WITH THAT!

SOFTY SPOTTY PERKINS

THERE!

GNOT WEARING THAT!

GNASH!

LET'S TRY THIS ELASTIC COLLAR.

S-T-R-E-T-C-H

BATH TIME, GNASHER!

GNO CHANCE!

COME BACK, GNASHER!

SNAG

GNOPE!

YOU CAME BACK! GOOD DOG!

SPLOOSH!

PYONNG

ELASTIC'S NO GOOD EITHER!

THAT DOES IT—NO COLLARS FOR ME!

IT'S FOR YOUR OWN GOOD, GNASHER!

BEST SAUSAGES

CAN'T HAVE HIM PICKED UP BY THE DOG CATCHER!

ZOOM!

LASSO

GLOOP!

THAT'S ONE COLLAR GNASHER DOESN'T MIND!

CHOMP!

CHEW!